More Beautiful than Flowers

MORE
BEAUTIFUL
THAN
FLOWERS

Joan M. Lexau

Drawings by Don Bolognese

J. B. LIPPINCOTT COMPANY
Philadelphia · New York

FOR

Eileen and Henry Lexau

AND

Elaine, Marisa, and Anne Marie Bolognese

Text copyright © 1966 by Joan M. Lexau

Illustrations copyright © 1966 by Donald Bolognese

PRINTED IN THE UNITED STATES OF AMERICA

Library of Congress Catalog Card Number 66–10903

More Beautiful than Flowers

I love You, God, for You are more beautiful than flowers,

more mysterious than the evening shadows,
more awesome than the highest mountain,

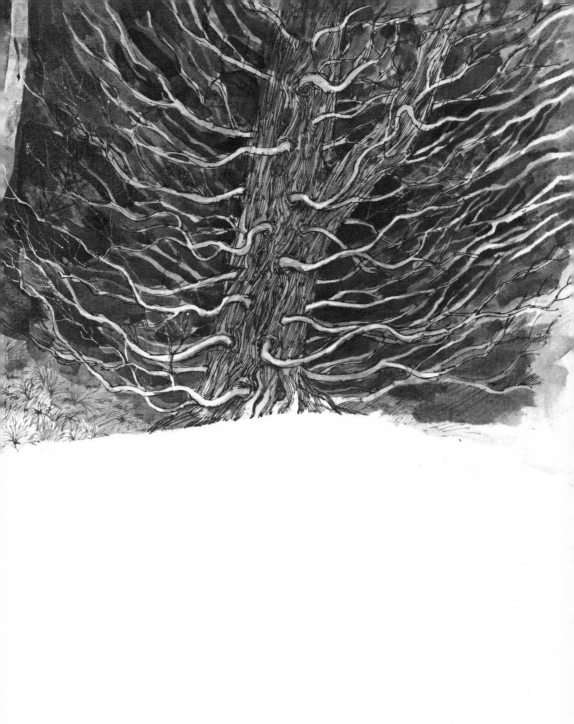

wiser than all the teachers in the world,
more just than the fairest judge,
more powerful than a thousand kings,
fiercer than a raging storm,

gentler than a mother and father with a newborn child,

more peaceful than a turtle napping,
older than the sand and sky.

I love You, God, for You can see all time at once,
the dinosaurs from long ago and life a million years from now.
You can count every drop of water in all the seas and oceans.
You are more unchanging than the order of the seasons,

more generous than a full moon in the dark of night,
more solemn than the deepest hush,

more joyous than the singing of birds at dawn.

I love You, God, for when I am sorry for being bad,
Your forgiveness is like sunshine after rain.

You are more certain than that night follows day,
larger than the universe,
closer to me than the air I breathe.
You know me better than I know myself.

You made me, love me, watch over each step I take,
and hear my every thought.
I love You, God, for some day I will be with You
if I will love You and do the things You ask.